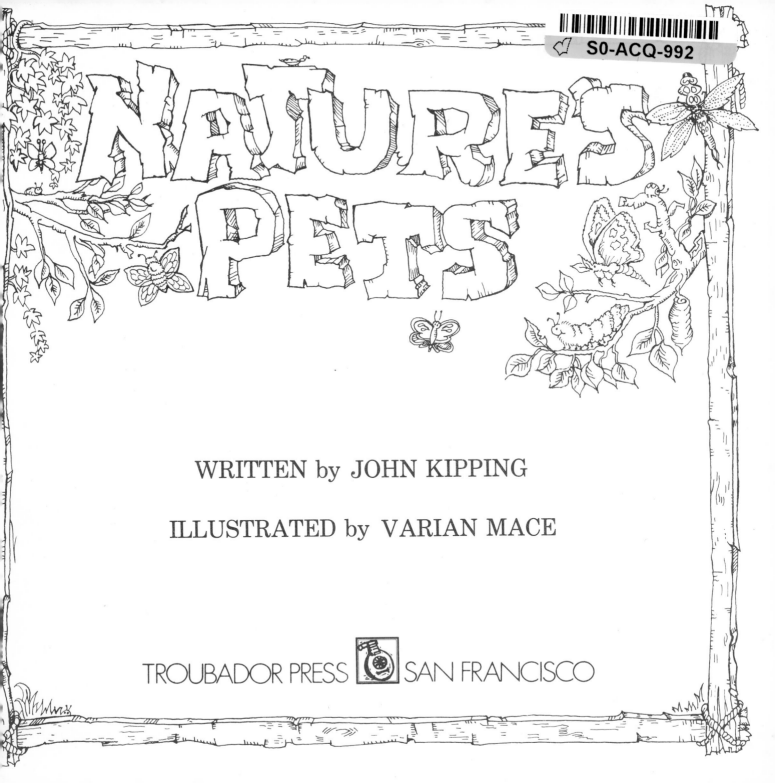

NATURE'S PETS

WRITTEN by JOHN KIPPING

ILLUSTRATED by VARIAN MACE

TROUBADOR PRESS SAN FRANCISCO

TABLE OF CONTENTS

CARE, CONSERVATION AND CONSIDERATION

Before removing an animal from its natural environment and placing it in a cage, you must learn something about its way of life, feeding habits, times of activity and any special requirements. When a creature becomes your pet, you are responsible for its health and well-being. Some small animals require special kinds of food and you may have to devote a considerable amount of time to finding the proper kind of diet. A pet's quarters must be kept clean and supplied with fresh water every day. If some pets are ignored for very long, they may die. You might wish to keep some of the small common animals mentioned in this book for a few weeks and then release them. This is easily done with native animals from your neighborhood. Animals from pet stores, however, often come from distant places and can't survive when released in your neighborhood. Sometimes unwanted or ill exotic animals can be donated to your local zoo or junior museum.

Some kinds of animals, including the Desert Tortoise and American Alligator, are protected by law and should never be caught and kept as pets. Actually, no alligator relatives should be purchased, as this will contribute to their decline in the wild. Other interesting and common animals may prove very difficult to maintain outside of their environments. For this reason tide pool animals (star fish, sea urchins, crabs, etc.) may be studied, but should be left in their habitats. The animals discussed in this book are found near home or commonly available in pet stores, and do not require much space or special equipment. If you simply give them the care and attention deserved by all living things, the creatures will be great pets and friends.

CAGES AND TERRARIA

The best all-around cage for many of Nature's Pets is a glass aquarium. Allowing view of the animal from all sides, the glass is easily cleaned, retains no odors, and can be adapted for fish, insects, reptiles, and small mammals. Used as a terrarium, it will need a pet-proof top. This is simply made with a four-sided wooden frame which is covered with hardware cloth mesh. Aquariums have the dis-advantage of being breakable and sometimes expensive. If you or a friend are handy with simple tools, you can put together a good cage of three wooden sides, a bottom, and a glass front.

Tack two thin wooden strips to either side of the front and slide a piece of glass into place (most hardware stores will cut the glass to fit). Cover the top edge of the glass with heavy tape for safety. A hinged top can be made from a piece of thin plywood or heavy cardboard. Cut a rectangular ventilation hole in the center of the top and cover it with fine screen or hardware cloth.

The wooden cage can be made moisture-proof for amphibians by using water sealers on wood and around the edges. Reptiles will need heat and light. You can use an aquarium hood, a gooseneck lamp or make your own as follows:

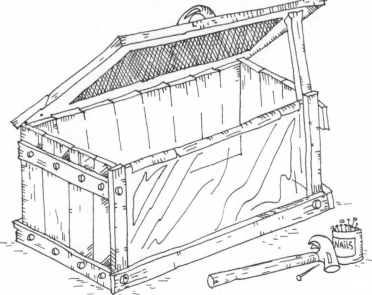

Making a Reflector Lamp for Terrariums

1. Buy bread pan (aluminum is best), light socket, light bulb and cord at a hardware store.

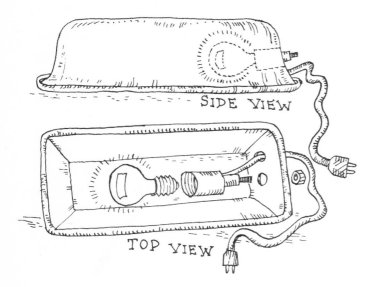

2. Remove retaining washer from switch extension of socket. Measure diameter of the extension and cut a slightly larger hole in middle of one end of the bread pan. Make small hole with hammer and nail. Then use screw driver or tang of a file to enlarge to proper size. Make another ¼" hole for lamp cord; this hole should be about 1¼" to one side of first hole.

3. Stick end of cord through cord hole and attach end to socket.

4. Put switch end of lamp socket through its hole and tighten retaining screw. Plug in.

5. Extra electrical tape wrapped about section of cord passing through hole will give protection against rubbing.

6. For a five gallon terrarium, a 40 watt bulb is best. For a ten gallon size cage, use 60 watt bulb.

Many small pets, such as frogs, salamanders, insects, earthworms, and fish, can be well housed in clean gallon jars used for pickles, mayonnaise, or mustard. The pets need air. Take the lid and punch many holes in it with a hammer and thin nail. These holes have jagged edges which should be smoothed by turning the lid upside down on a sidewalk and pounding them flat with a hammer. ·

SNAKES

Snakes are fascinating animals and most are readily tamed. With a few special "do's," most species will succeed in captivity. You should keep only those snakes which are native to your area so they can be released if they don't adjust to cage life. Exotic snakes, with the possible exception of boa constrictors, shouldn't be purchased. Snakes are "cold-blooded," that is, they don't have an even body temperature. If the cage is too cold, the reptiles will be sluggish; too high a temperature can be fatal. If kept at about 70-75°F (21-24°C), most snakes will be comfortable.

Almost all snakes will eat only live food and you should consult a reptile book to learn of each species' food habits. Some eat only worms, salamanders or frogs, while others eat mice or baby chickens. A few are cannibalistic. Garter and water snakes get by quite well on a diet of frogs and can even be coaxed into eating small pieces of fish. Most constricting or squeezing snakes, such as the Bull, Gopher, Corn, and Kingsnake, will eat mice purchased from pet stores. Young chicks are available for these constrictors from poultry farms, feed stores, and hatcheries and are inexpensive.

Most adult snakes need to feed only once every two to four weeks. Snakes should not be handled for a day before feeding and for several days afterwards; if upset, a snake will often throw up its last meal. When a mouse is put in the cage, include a little food for it. If the snake does not eat the mouse in a short time, remove the mouse from the cage. Never leave the mouse in the cage overnight. Hungry mice have been known to chew on pet snakes!

COMMON GARTER SNAKE

WATER SNAKE

Snakes need a bowl of clean water for drinking and bathing. Before shedding their old outer skin, snakes will often soak themselves in water for a few hours. When your pet is about to shed its old clothing, its skin becomes dull-toned and the eyes appear bluish. Your pet will need a sharp-edged rock or rough tree bark in the cage to rub against to start shedding.

The best snake cage is a glass terrarium with a tight-fitting lid. Cover the top with hardware cloth, not wire screen, because some nervous snakes will rub against it constantly in trying to escape and they can rub their snouts raw. The cage bottom can be pea gravel or folded newspaper. The paper is clean, easily changed and, unlike sand or gravel, can't get caught in the snake's mouth when eating. The heat source can be either a room heater or a lamp reflector placed on top of the cage. A 40 watt bulb is usually sufficient for light and warmth in a 5 to 10 gallon tank. It's a good idea to turn off the lights at night, unless the room temperature will drop too low. Since some snakes are nervous, try to provide them with a place of retreat such as a flat rock or piece of bark.

Both snakes and lizards in the wild are likely to have parasites called mites. These tick relatives can become a serious problem with captive reptiles but are harmless to humans. Keep the cage clean by washing it with hot soapy water and changing the rocks and wood cage decorations when needed. The mites can be killed by dusting the snake with flea or mite powder, leaving it for an hour, and then washing it off. A flea collar placed in the cage for a few hours is another effective means of controlling these tiny pests. Another problem of captive snakes is found in some that soak themselves too much and develop fungus infections in their skin which look like small whitish lumps. Let the snake stay dry for a couple of weeks and it should clear up.

KING SNAKE

LIZARDS

Like snakes, lizards need warmth for activity. Food is easy to obtain, since these reptiles readily eat spiders and insects. Most pet and bait stores will sell you mealworms (beetle larvae) and crickets. If you would rather get your own, you can catch many insects around the neighborhood. Moths are easily captured near lights at night. Many earwigs can be collected by rolling up some newspaper or cardboard to put under some bushes. Pick up the papers in a few days and shake into a bucket. A few boards left around the garden will attract crickets and other lizard delicacies. In winter when wild insects are unavailable, you will probably have to buy mealworms.

FENCE LIZARD

Lizards should be housed like snakes: both need escape-proof housing. Geckos and Anoles (American Chameleons) can climb glass walls. The cage bottom can be covered with paper or coarse sand. Horned Lizards and Skinks like to bury themselves in sand at night and should be provided with this material. Most other lizards like rocky hiding places, but the stones should be carefully arranged to prevent shifting and possible injury. Remember that some large species such as Leopard, Collared and Spiny Lizards will eat smaller specimens, so separate your pet lizards according to their sizes.

SKINK

AMERICAN ANOLE
(CHAMELEON)

Fence Lizards or Blue Belly Lizards are found throughout the United States and make fine pets. They are often available at pet stores or can be captured with a little patience and stalking. Use a slip knot of fine copper wire hung from the end of a pole. Gradually approach a sunning lizard and try to slip the loop over its head. Quickly lift up and then remove the slip noose. Handle these small animals gently. Remember that most lizards can lose their tails when they are pulled. Think about conservation and don't catch more than a couple of lizards.

Green Iguanas from Mexico are popular pets. Many Iguanas are sold each year, but few survive to reach their full five to six feet in length. A healthy Iguana will eat a great variety of foods, including fresh fruit and vegetables. Dried alfalfa can be used when fresh greens are unavailable. Some of the healthiest Iguanas seen are those which have been coaxed into eating moist dog food as part of their diets. Handle your Iguanas with care as large ones have long sharp claws and whip-like tails. After some time in captivity, most will become quite docile. These are intelligent lizards and will soon come to know you when you approach the cage. One fun trick to play with a male Iguana is to place

GECKOS

a mirror in the cage. Thinking another male is in his territory, your Iguana will display his throat bib in warning.

You can buy water-soluble vitamins from pet stores and add a couple of drops to the food or water. On warm sunny days allow your Iguana to sun bathe for a few hours. The ultraviolet rays of sunlight are important to the animals because they help them make vitamin D. If you have a sun lamp at home, give your pet reptiles about ten minutes a week and they will be much more active and healthy.

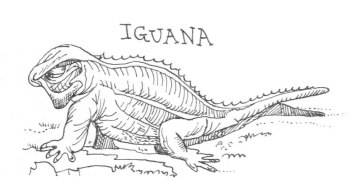

IGUANA

Turtles and Tortoises

Turtles are extremely well-adapted for their watery existence. The hard shell is streamlined and the turtle's webbed hind feet aid in rapid swimming. Turtles are long-lived and can be excellent pets if their few needs are met. Provide them with fresh water in a large fish bowl or aquarium. This should be kept at or above room temperature, since reptiles are cold-blooded. Turtles also need a place to dry off. Pet turtles kept in water for long periods may develop fungal infections known as "soft shell."

Most turtles are meat eaters and their diet should include chopped liver, horsemeat, fish, earthworms, or insects. When feeding meat, occasionally dip it in bone meal (available at pet stores). The bone meal provides calcium which your turtle needs for strong shell growth. Never buy a turtle which has a painted shell because the paint may already have injured it. Change the water every other day, as turtles are quite messy. You can provide vitamins by giving the turtles some spinach or lettuce weekly.

Tortoises are land-going varieties of turtles and are plant hunters. Although they are slow swimmers, they seem to appreciate a dip and long drinks once in awhile. Tortoises are great at digging, in fact, one species is known as the Gopher Tortoise. It is a common occurence for them to escape from gardens by tunneling under fences. Therefore, you will need a large enclosure to keep them from roaming. Keep large dogs away from your pet. Small tortoises can be kept inside a large wooden or cardboard box with soil in the bottom and a light for heat. Feed fresh fruit and vegetables. On warm days let them mow your lawn because they like to eat grass. Many types of tortoises can be bought at pet stores, but some native species are protected by law. Check with your wildlife authorities before taking any from the wild.

TORTOISE

POND TURTLE

15

Tadpoles are the young of frogs and toads. These animals belong to an ancient group of back-boned animals known as amphibians. This means "two lives," because they start life as eggs and larvae in water, then undergo a wonderful change to become land creatures. The eggs are laid singly or in masses in or on the water or attached to aquatic (meaning, living in or on the water) plants. The legless, tailed tadpole uses food reserves in its tail for the first day or two, but soon must find algae to eat.

Put your tadpoles or eggs into a large pan or aquarium and fill with cool pond water. The tadpoles will thrive on pond weeds, cooked spinach, chopped meat and boiled eggs. Don't put too much food in at one time because it can foul the water. Change the water every other day, or use an aquarium air pump to keep the water full of oxygen.

Since crowding is harmful, never keep more than a dozen tadpoles together. Watch your pets as they grow and start sprouting first hind and then fore legs. The tail will disappear while other changes are taking place inside. The digestive tract becomes much shorter, the lungs grow and a real mouth with jaws and teeth appear. The tadpole is now a frog or toad. Until this time the tadpole breathed with gills. You can study this by taking an eye dropper with food coloring and squirting a drop in front of the mouth. Watch where the color comes out. The coloring is harmless to the pet. You will want to provide something for them to crawl onto as they mature. A floating piece of wood or a sloping sand bottom will allow movement from water to land. Some kinds of tadpoles will make the change in a few weeks while others, such as bull frogs, can require up to three years.

FROGS AND TOADS

Tadpoles eventually grow into adult frogs or toads which have food and housing needs different from their larvae, or early stage of development. Unlike reptiles, these amphibians have skin which can become dry and result in the animals' death. You must provide a moist habitat, especially for frogs. A terrarium with part water, part land is ideal. The water should be kept cool and clean.

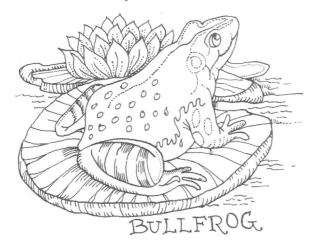

BULLFROG

Toads are better adjusted for land life than frogs and can be kept in a cage with wet coarse sand in which they will burrow. Add some small potted plants for color and fresh air. Both frogs and toads will eat just about anything which moves and is smaller than themselves: earthworms, spiders, insects and small pieces of fish or meat wiggled in front of them. Watch how quickly the tongue is slipped out to catch the food and how the amphibian's eyes close down. Larger bits of food are pushed into the big mouth with help from the front legs. Feed your animals every other day.

When handling your pets, always wet your hands to help protect their delicate skins. When picking up toads, hold them away from yourself, as they will usually release the water they have stored. A good way to catch these critters is to visit ponds and marshes during Spring breeding season. At night listen for the males' calls and then point a flashlight in the direction of the sound. When the beam strikes a frog, you will see a bright reflection. While the light still hits its eyes, the frog will not move and you can approach it slowly. They can be carried home in a moistened container, preferably unbreakable.

TOAD

SALAMANDERS

Salamanders are sluggish amphibians often mistaken for lizards. One important difference between these two animals is that salamanders have moist skin. This gives us a clue to their habits and whereabouts. Most salamanders prefer dark moist homes. When you search for them, turn over rocks, logs and bark, always replacing these hiding places as you found them. Some types of salamanders can be found in ponds and streams, especially during breeding season: late fall or early spring. Certain salamanders, known as newts, live on land as adults, but return to water to lay their eggs. The Western Newt sometimes travels as far as two miles to return to favored breeding ponds. One community recently put up highway signs warning motorists of a popular newt crossing. If you collect a few salamanders, they can be carried home in a moistened coffee can. Remember, don't let them dry out!

Salamanders are secretive; that is, they like to have a hiding place. You can plant a terrarium with mosses, ferns, and other woodland plants. Sphagnum Moss, available at plant stores, makes an ideal covering. Prepare the terrarium with one-half inch of aquarium charcoal and an equal amount of coarse sand. Mix these and then add about two inches of good garden soil. After planting your friend's home, keep it moist. Because amphibians survive best at cool temperatures, the terrarium should be kept away from direct sunlight.

MUD SALAMANDER

All salamanders eat live food such as earthworms, spiders and small insects. Try coaxing them to eat tiny pieces of meat dangled from a slender twig. One American salamander sometimes sold in pet stores is called the Red-Spotted Newt. When kept in a terrarium they are reddish orange, but when placed in an aquarium, they change color and become dull green with red spots. You might experiment with these to see how many days the color changes take.

RED SPOTTED NEWT

MINI-POND

In your aquarium you can keep several interesting small native fish, netted from creeks and ponds. Sticklebacks, Minnows, Shiners, Darters, and the young of Perch, Bluegill, Catfish, Pickerel, and Suckers are all fun to raise. They need cool, clean water and ample oxygen; therefore their aquarium should have several well-established water plants or an aquarium air pump. When fish of different species are kept together, watch carefully to make sure they get along. Release troublemakers or keep in another tank. Don't try to keep more than a half dozen fish in a five gallon fish tank. Feed your pets chopped earthworms, meat, fish, hard-boiled eggs, or tropical fish food. Try feeding them a little bit

at a time. If you notice extra food in the tank, you are giving them too much.

Sometimes you will be able to find fresh water clams and snails. These can be kept with some small fish, but will need different foods. Clams feed by filtering the water and digesting any edible tidbits. You will have to give them fresh pond water every two days. The snails will eat the algae which grows on the sides of the aquarium; they will also eat spinach.

Crayfish may sometimes be housed with true fish, but these fresh water cousins of lobsters seem to have crabby dispositions and may fight — either with the fish or each other. When frightened, this remarkable animal can skip backwards with one powerful stroke of its tail. Look for crayfish among rocks or sunken branches in streams and ponds. Tie some meat bait on a string or a fishing line and pull them ashore. When handling a crayfish, pick it up with thumb and forefinger just behind the powerful pincher legs. Keep the aquarium water clean by replacing it with new stream or pond water twice a week. Feed the crayfish chopped earthworms, meat or fish. Don't have more than a few in one tank, because they may fight and hurt each other.

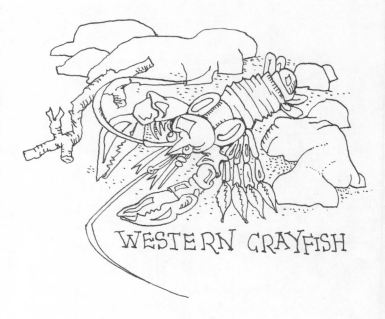

WESTERN CRAYFISH

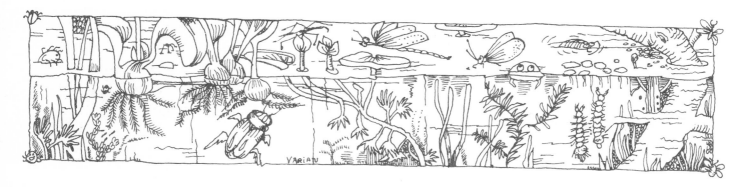

WATER INSECTS*

If you have enjoyed keeping small fish, you shouldn't miss the adventure of watching water insects. Beneath the surface of any pond are thousands of these strange and interesting creatures. A small fish net with a long handle is ideal for scooping swimming or crawling insects from the water. Empty the net into a bucket of water to see what you have caught. Once home, place your new pets in a fish bowl, gallon jar or aquarium. The tank should have a good supply of fresh pond water, some gravel on the bottom and a few algae-covered rocks from the insects' home pond. The algae will be eaten by some of your water pets. Other animals such as the larval Dragonfly, Damselfly and adult Diving Beetles will need to be fed other small insects. Use a butterfly net to sweep over grasses and bushes to catch many tiny insects such as plant bugs, small caterpillers, flies and bees. Dump your catch into the aquarium.

Some aquatic insects can fly at any time and many of the others will grow wings when they shed their skins for the last time. The aquarium should have a screened top to prevent escapes. The insects that will have wings need a few stems or reeds to climb out of the water. They can then shed their skin and dry their wings. Once the Dragon and Damselflies have matured, they are difficult to keep alive and should be freed. An extra reward of keeping a healthy water insect collection is watching the growth and changes from juvenile to adult.

If pond water is not easily obtained, you can use cool tap water if it is not chlorinated. Ask your parents or teacher about this. The chlorine can be removed by letting a bucket of water stand for two days before it's used. Some pet stores sell tablets to remove chlorine from the water. Never place your jars or aquariums on a window sill where direct sunlight will hit them for more than a few minutes. The water can quickly heat up and harm your pets.

CATERPILLERS

VARIAN

Caterpillars are the larvae (worm-like young) of moths and butterflies. You can become an amateur lepidopterist (a person who studies moths and butterflies — the insect order *Lepidoptera*) by observing these fascinating insects at home. Almost every caterpillar feeds on plants. Keep a sharp lookout for these critters while on your way to school or in the garden. Most caterpillars are quite choosy about the kind of plants they eat. Pay special attention to the type of plant you find them on, because you'll have to collect the same kind of leaves or flowers to feed your growing caterpillar. For instance, Monarch butterflies eat milkweeds, Satyrs prefer grasses, Painted Ladies enjoy thistles and mallows, and the sulfur and white butterflies eat plants belonging to the pea and mustard families.

Watch for butterflies that swoop through plants quickly. They are probably females laying eggs. To collect the tiny eggs take some of the plant on which the eggs were laid. After they hatch, the young caterpillars will have to be brought fresh food every other day. As the caterpillar grows, it will shed, or molt, its skin. This occurs about four times. After the final molting, it becomes restless and will seek a place to form a chrysalis or spin a cocoon. This is the pupa stage when the wondrous change to adulthood takes place.

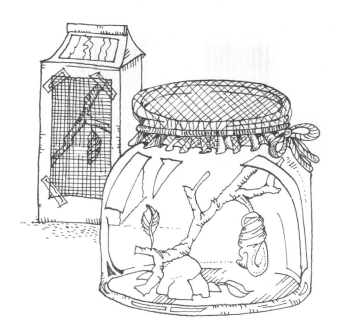

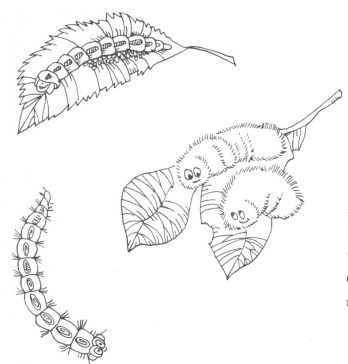

A caterpillar cage can be almost anything: a shoe box, milk carton, or cereal box with a cellophane window and screened air passage taped on one side. Give the animals a few drops of water each day on the plant food.

Butterfly larvae make their cocoons on twigs, while many kinds of moth larvae will burrow into soft earth. After emerging, the new butterfly will climb up on a branch and pump blood into its new wings until they are expanded and dried. Adults can be kept and fed a diluted mixture of honey, but it's a better idea to release them to reproduce.

23

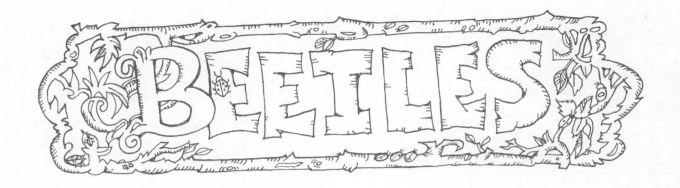

BEETLES

If Noah had managed to put every kind of animal into his ark, one out of every five passengers would have been a beetle. Several common types of beetles can make good pets. Some of the best are large shiny black Darkling Beetles. These slow-moving beetles are flightless, since their upper pair of hard wings are fused together. Darkling Beetles can be seen wandering about in dry areas. When disturbed, some will do a handstand and perhaps release a bad smell. These beetles can be kept for years in a glass bowl or terrarium and fed bits of dry dog food or pieces of potato. Keep a small piece of sponge in one part of the cage and wet this every week.

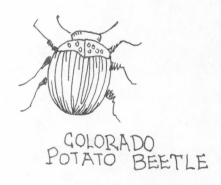

COLORADO POTATO BEETLE

Mealworms, or Golden Grubs, are the larva of the Darkling Beetle. They can be purchased at pet and fishing bait stores and are easily raised. Keep them in a box or tray filled two inches deep with corn or bran meal. Place several strips of cloth or paper in the meal to prevent it from becoming tightly packed. The mealworms grow larger and shed their skins. When they are nearly an inch long, they molt the skin and become pupae, which look half way like adult beetles and half way like the wormy larvae. This is the resting stage during which the

DARKLING BEETLE

LADYBUG

Lady Beetles are interesting, but demanding pets. These brightly colored beetles are good for our gardens and farms because they eat plant pests. If you want to keep some at home, you will have to bring them many pests to eat. Look for masses of tiny, round insects called Aphids on the tips of green plants. Aphids come in all colors and sizes and may or may not have wings.

LEAF BEETLE

pupa changes to an adult. The black adults mate, lay eggs and die, but thousands of young will soon hatch. Besides the cereals, you can feed them vegetable scraps, as well as stale bread and crackers. Mealworms raised in your house can be used as food for many other small animals.

Fireflies or Lightning Bugs are really beetles, not flies or bugs. The eerie glowing light which some varieties have helps the beetles locate each other at night for mating. In tropical areas several kinds may all be seen flashing, but with different signals. During the day the light spots on the beetle are

FIREFLY

yellow-green. The light produced by the spots is cold and about ten times more efficient than an electric light bulb. The larvae eat other insects, but you can feed the adults flowers. Catch some and see them light up a dark room.

CUCUMBER BEETLE

ANTS

Of all the recognizable animals on earth, ants are perhaps the most numerous. The hundreds of species have developed many interesting ways of life. There are some which take care of aphids or plant lice much as we take care of dairy cattle. Other ants make a living by raiding rival colonies and enslaving them. Still others cut leaves off plants and take them underground to raise fungus gardens for food.

To keep a successful ant farm, you must collect the queen ant, the only ant that can reproduce and keep up the morale of the workers. Look for ant colonies under fallen logs or large rocks. Once you have located a colony, dig down carefully and look for an ant which is much bigger than the others: this is the queen. Take the queen, a few dozen workers, and some of the grub-like pupae.

The ants can be put into a large glass jar filled to within two inches of the top with rich, loose soil. Cover the outer sides with black paper and remove this only while you are observing them. The best kind of ant cage is the observation nest, or "ant farm." You can buy these at pet or toy stores or make your own.

Build a wooden frame to hold two pieces of glass about three-quarters of an inch apart. The frame will need a fine wire mesh top and some corked holes for inserting food. A small piece of sponge in a corner can be wetted for proper humidity. Keep the sides covered by black paper when not observing, otherwise the ants will not build tunnels near the glass.

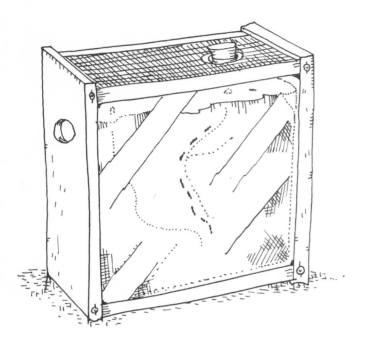

Experiment with various foods to find the proper diet for your pets. Try small dead insects caught by sweeping bushes with a butterfly net. Weed seeds are sometimes eaten, or try placing aphids inside the cage. Aphids can be found on most garden plants. Look for masses of tiny insects near the ends of branches. Aphids come in all sizes and colors, some have wings and others don't.

CRICKETS AND THEIR COUSINS

Field crickets occur in most regions of the United States and are more often heard than seen. The males sing together — serenading the females. The sounds are produced when the forewings are rapidly rubbed together. The calls or chirps are more rapid and higher pitched in warm weather. It is possible to tell the temperature by counting the chirps in one minute and then applying the following formula: temperature (degrees Fahrenheit) $= 50 + \dfrac{\text{number of chirps} - 40}{4}$. This is the formula for a house cricket. Look for these insects at night with a flashlight or under boards during daylight. They can be kept in any kind of closed cage and fed almost any kitchen scrap, especially potatoes. Give the cage a light misting of water every other day or keep a small piece of wet sponge in the cage.

CRICKET

The Praying Mantis looks like a Hollywood monster. Not only is it a strange appearing animal, but quite voracious, eating anything of similar size

which moves. The Mantis is actually quite gentle and tame in captivity when handled carefully. Hatching from a frothy-looking egg case, the numerous tiny mantises soon crawl over plants in search of food. They slowly approach another insect and snatch it with their large front "praying" legs. Mantises can be kept for six to seven months before they die. Their cage can be a large jar with a lid or you can make a shoe box terrarium. The cage will need some branches for climbing, lots of insects for food, and water mist for a drinking fountain. Look for the Mantis in shrubs or buy egg cases from biological control dealers.

COCKROACH

Cockroaches are misunderstood creatures. Although they become household pests, they do not spread disease. In captivity, they are clean and show remarkable intelligence for an insect. Normally, these swift, flat-bodied ancient insects avoid light. Your pet will soon adapt to illumination. Be sure that the cage is escape proof. Cockroaches are not finicky about food. You can give them any leftovers from the kitchen. A fun way of testing their intelligence is to build a maze. Put some food at one end and release the cockroach at the other

end. Use a watch and record how long it takes the roach to reach the reward. Try the experiment several times to see how quickly the lesson is learned.

Cockroach, Cricket or Beetle Maze

A maze can be made from a cardboard box with paper walls glued or taped down in the pattern shown below. Or create your own pattern. The maze should be covered with a piece of carefully taped down glass, clear plastic, or saran wrap. Peanut butter can be placed at one end for the reward.

SPIDERS

Next to snakes, spiders are probably the most misunderstood animals. When the average person sees a spider, the usual reaction is to crush it. Spiders can be poisonous, but only a few kinds in the United States are dangerous to humans. The Black Widow is common in many places and makes large cobwebs. Only the female bites and she is easily recognized: about one half-inch long, shiny black with a red hourglass marking on the underside. Black Widows are usually found on their webs under objects near houses, trash, outhouses, and dumps. Two relatives, the Brown Widow of Florida and the Northern Widow, have similar red markings. The Brown Recluse Spider of Texas, Oklahoma and Missouri can inflict severe bites which take months to heal. This half-inch brown spider lives in houses, behind furniture or on the floor.

Yet, several spiders make interesting, safe pets. Tarantulas are large hairy ground spiders found in the dry plains, grasslands, and deserts in the United

States. They can be found walking along roads at dusk or dawn when they venture from their burrows in search of insects. They are fairly slow and soon become tame in captivity. It is possible to allow them to crawl onto your hand and pick them up. Be gentle.

TARANTULA

Tarantulas can be kept in a terrarium or large glass jars. Make a close-fitting top because these animals can climb glass walls. Your pet will need live food such as mealworms and crickets. The cage bottom should be covered with loose soil. Provide a hiding place of rocks or small pieces of wood. Fill a jar top with water for your spider to drink.

Garden spiders make beautiful large circular orb webs in shrubs and trees. The webs are quite visible after rainy or dewy weather. These spiders are about three-quarters of an inch long and usually have bright orange abdomens and various black and white markings. They don't stay in the middle of their webs, but hide under a curled leaf on a nearby branch. Although Garden Spiders have poor vision, they keep in touch with their web by holding a signal line to their legs. When the spider feels a small tug, it scrambles down the line to wrap up its catch. Try wiggling the web to see if you can fool the spider. *Argiope* Spiders are also orb-weavers, but have brilliant black and yellow or silver markings and banded legs. They hang upside down in the center of their webs, which usually have some zigzag bands.

Catch your orb weaver and take her (most big spiders seen are females) home in a jar. Use a large glass jar or terrarium with some shrub branches. Watch how the web is constructed, for it is a miracle of engineering. Feed your pet one or two flies or mealworms a week. Give the cage a light misting of water with a window spray bottle each week.

EARTHWORMS

Earthworms are the recyclers of the soil. Within a single acre there may be from 25,000 to one million worms, each eating its way through and enriching the soil. From ten to one hundred tons of soil pass through these worms each year. Worms add calcium to the soil, improve its texture and help water and air penetrate. Earthworms can be found in most soils and make useful, interesting pets.

Carefully dig up several worms and place them in a pan, tray or small wooden box filled two-thirds with moist soil and leaves. Keep the soil moist by covering the top loosely with plastic or burlap cloth. Your pets will eat any kitchen leftovers, as well as leaves and manure. Your worm corral should be placed in a cool location, perhaps a shady corner of the garden. In cold winter areas, move your worm colony to a protected place to prevent freezing.

EARTHWORM

When you want to observe your worms, you will have to move their box to a darkened room or use a weak flash light at night. Worms normally come to the surface only at night or when the soil becomes water-logged. They hang their bodies part way out of their holes to drag small leaves under ground. If they feel a vibration, they quickly duck inside. The 19th century biologist Charles Darwin once experimented with earthworm intelligence. He cut leaves into various shapes to find if the worms were smart enough to turn the leaves the right way to fit into the holes. Try this experiment and keep a record of the results.

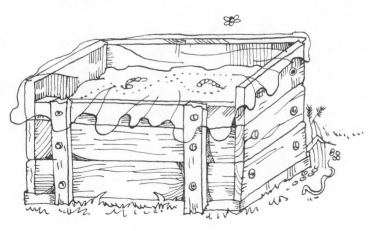

There are some benefits from your earthworm farm. The worms multiply quickly and can be used as food for pet reptiles and amphibians and the soil from their box makes excellent compost for vegetable gardening.

SNAILS AND SLUGS

These soft-bodied animals are the scourge of gardeners all over the world. For this reason, you shouldn't have much trouble finding plenty to keep as pets. Remember that these mollusks (from the Latin word for soft) are about 97% water and even with their abundant slime they can die if their cage dries out. The cage can be a one or two quart jar, or you may wish to keep them with your salamanders. Snails and slugs are both plant eaters, although slugs are known to eat dog and cat food left outside overnight. Make a note of which plants they prefer.

Look for these crawling animals on wet days or at night. On warm days, they usually hide under rocks and boards or in other dark places. You should have two of each kind in your cage if you want them to reproduce. Each snail and slug is both male and female. An interesting courtship can happen when two meet. After awhile, they give each other sperm to fertilize the numerous round, whitish eggs.

Snails and slugs are interesting to watch, especially as they climb up the glass walls. If you have caught water snails, you'll soon see them walking upside down across the water surface. Both snails and slugs have unusual eyes which are held on the end of retractable stalks. When something appears dangerous, these stalks are quickly drawn inside the head. Snails depend on their shells for protection, but slugs give off lots of bubbly slime when attacked by predators such as birds, toads, or hunting beetles.

MicRoScOPic ALGAE JunGle

If you are short on space for pets, why not try microscopic animals and plants? Some of the strangest and most beautiful life forms exist under our very eyes, but we can't see them without a microscope. If there is a microscope you can use at school, at home, or with a friend, you may spend many delightful hours exploring the world in a drop of water. Take a cup of pond water and a few bits of pond plants, place them in a jar, add a

tablespoon of garden soil, and set near a window for a few days.

Use an eye dropper to take a drop of water from the jar. Place the drop on a microscope slide and put a cover slip over it. Fit the slide on your microscope and explore the unseen world.

Most microscopic plants consist of only a few cells.

Some of the more common are diatoms or plants with interesting ornamental shells. These transparent shells come in many shapes, but most are circular or triangular. The 12,000 kinds of diatoms all have beautiful geometric patterns formed by tiny spines, dots, or lines. Fossil diatom shells are used today in toothpastes and in chemical filters. Other algae may have beautiful designs too. The green *Spirogyra* is a very common pond plant consisting of long thin cells attached end to end. Look for the two inter-twined spirals of green chlorophyll inside the cells.

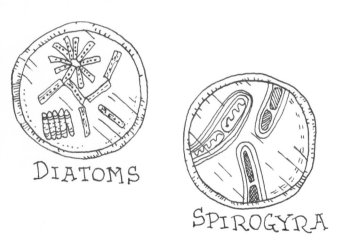

DIATOMS

SPIROGYRA

Among the animal life you will find with the microscope are amoebas. They look like little blobs of clear jelly. Amoebas move by stretching and changing shape. Watch them eat by surrounding bits of food with their bodies. If you're lucky, you might see one about to reproduce. Watch how it splits down the middle into two new animals. A frantic movement nearby may be from a tiny water flea, *Daphnia*, a cousin of the crayfish. *Daphnia* give birth to live young. You can see them inside the mother because she has a clear shell. A closely related creature is *Cyclops*, a little animal that

DAPHNIA

CYCLOPS

swims along carrying two bags of eggs. Its single eye gives this animal its name. Small flat worms, called *Planaria*, can be collected in ponds by putting small pieces of meat in the shallow water and then retrieving them in a few days. *Planaria* have flat triangular heads and two eyes.

Possibly the most interesting of all microscopic pets are the rotifers. These active animals appear to have tiny spinning wheels in their mouths. The spinning is the result of rapid movements of small hair-like tentacles around the mouth. The motion causes water to enter the mouth along with little bits of food and can help some rotifers move through the water. Some kinds of rotifers are swimmers, but others are attached to strands of green algae.

The *Hydra* is a fascinating animal which resembles a small transparent palm tree. The leaves of the palm are really tentacles which grab passing water fleas and other animals. These are pulled into the inside of the "trunk." The tentacles have little poisoned harpoons that paralyze the captured animals. When a *Hydra* needs to reproduce, it simply grows a new small baby from a little bud near its base. These buds, or polyps, grow, drop off the parent, and attach themselves to floating leaves and underwater plants. An excellent place to search for hydras is on duckweed, a small-leaved floating plant common on all ponds.

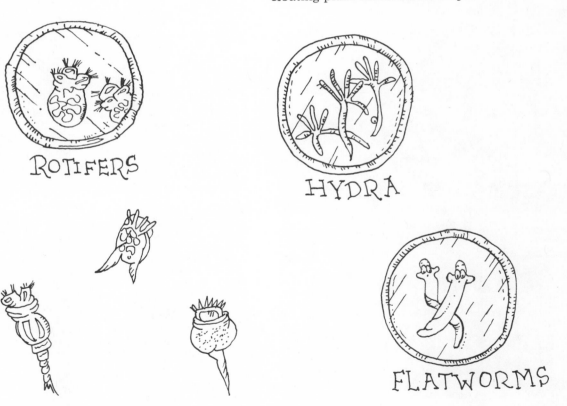

ROTIFERS

HYDRA

FLATWORMS

INSECTIVOROUS PLANTS

Most of us know that green plants can make their own food by using sunlight, water, carbon dioxide, and minerals from the soil. There are, however, a few which need a little help from the animal kingdom. These plants are mainly bog dwellers and have different devices for trapping animals and using their proteins. The Venus Fly Traps, the Sun Dews, the Cobra Plant, and the Pitcher Plants are found in various regions of the United States. If none occur near your home (check with your teacher or local museum), several kinds can be purchased from plant stores and nurseries.

To grow these plants well, you must make a miniature bog. Use a dish or shallow pan filled with damp peat and sphagnum moss mixed with light soil. Arrange your plants and always keep them very damp. You can give them a light misting of water every day if the leaf edges start to turn brown. If your water supply is "hard" or full of minerals, use bottled, distilled, or rainwater for best results. The chlorine in some water systems is harmful to these plants. Fill a bucket and let it stand overnight before using; this allows the chlorine gas to evaporate.

The Venus Flytrap catches small insects by snapping the two halves of its leaves together when the animals touch the small triggers on the inner leaf surfaces. You can easily over-feed your plant. Always wait for one meal to be digested before

SUNDEW PLANT

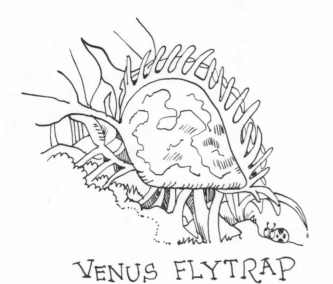

VENUS FLYTRAP

PITCHER PLANT

serving another helping. Keep a record of how long this takes. The Sundew Plant glistens because of its sticky hairs. These trap tiny flies which aren't strong enough to escape. If the leaves aren't soon covered with insects, put a piece of ripe fruit near your plant for a few days; your plant will soon be well fed. Pitcher and Cobra Plants have large hollow leaves. Keep these half-filled with water and feed them a fly every week.

Other Books of Interest About Nature's Pets

Brown, V. *How to Make a Miniature Zoo.* Little, Brown & Co. New York. 1957.

Johnson, G. and M. Bleifeld. *Hunting With the Microscope.* Sentinel Books. New York. 1963.

Levi, H.W. and Levi, L.R. *A Guide to Spiders and Their Kin.* Golden Press. New York. 1968.

Reid, G.K. *Pond Life. A Guide to Common Plants and Animals of North American Ponds and Lakes.* Golden Press. New York. 1967.

Snedigar, R. *Our Small Native Animals: Their Habits and Care.* Dover Publications, Inc. New York. 1963.

Zim, H.S. and Cottam, C. *A Guide to Familiar American Insects.* Golden Press. New York. 1951.

Some Sources of Supplies for Nature's Pets

Supplies for mealworms:

Surelive Mealworm Company
22536 Halldale Avenue
Torrance, Ca.

Supplies for crickets:

Fluker's Cricket Farm
2623 Beach Street
Baton Rouge, La.

Sources for aquariums and terrariums:

Ward's Biological Supply Co.
P.O. Box 1749
Monterey, Ca. 93940

Varian

MORE ENTERTAINING BOOKS FROM TROUBADOR PRESS

ACTIVITY BOOKS

Auto Racing Color and Story	$2.00
Beasties Color Book	2.00
Dinosaur Color Book	2.00
Fat Cat Coloring and Limerick Book	2.00
Fifty Years of Cars — Models to Make	2.00
Geometric Playthings — Cut and Build	2.00
Kachina Dolls Cut Outs	2.00
Los Angeles Scenes	2.00
Love Bug Color and Limerick Book	2.00
Monster Gallery Color and Story Book	2.00
New York Scenes	2.00
North American Birdlife Coloring Album	2.00
North American Sealife Coloring Album	2.00
North American Wildflowers Coloring Album	2.00
North American Wildlife Coloring Album	2.00
New Testament Color and Story Book	2.00
Old Testament Color and Story Book	2.00
Paper Airplanes — Color Fold and Fly	2.00
Paper Movie Machines — Ready to Make	2.00
San Francisco Scenes	2.00
Science Fiction Anthology — Color and Story	2.00
Zodiac Color Book	2.00

FAT CAT FUN BOOKS

A Child's American Heritage	1.50
Fat Cat's Cookbook	1.50
Fat Cat's Craftbook	1.50
It's Your World Ecology Book	1.50
Meanings of Christmas	1.50
Nature Crafts and Projects	1.50
Once Upon A Time	1.50
Small World Cookbook	1.50

TROUBADOR SPECIALS

International Folk Crafts	$1.50
Monster Movie Game	2.00
Nature's Pets	1.50
Optricks	1.50
Optricks II	1.50
Think Metrics	1.50

GIFT EDITIONS

Aphrodisiac Cookery (hb)	4.95
The Bath Book (hb)	5.95
The Bath Book (pb)	2.95
The Scrimshander (pb)	6.95
Sprouting Cookbook (hb)	5.95
Sprouting Cookbook (pb)	3.95
Yogurt Cookbook (pb)	3.95

PUZZLEBOOKS

Computer Crosswords	1.50
Maze Craze	1.50
Maze Craze II	1.50
Maze Craze III	1.50
Puzzlers	1.50

TROUBADOR PRESS · 126 FOLSOM STREET · SAN FRANCISCO, CA 94105